PENGUIN BOOKS

THE LAWS OF CAT PHYSICS

G. A. Mendenhall lives alone with his wife and three cats in Green Valley, Arizona. He is partially colourblind and adamantly insists that green, orange and pink are merely different shades of the same colour. So far, he has carefully avoided formal art training and is almost completely housebroken.

Mendenhall started writing and cartooning in 1985 while recovering from a botched vasectomy performed by a redoubtable and somewhat shaky urologist. The eventual result was a cartoon panel called 'Business as Usual' and the book you are hopefully buying, not just perusing.

The author was raised on the US–Mexico border and did not speak English until the age of six, when he discovered it was the best language for humour and cursing. He admits to having university degrees in English and Political Science. Like most writers, he is motivated by a combination of fear, greed, envy and self-doubt.

He often writes all night, which makes him an unbearable grouch during normal daylight hours. He gets many of his ideas while vacuuming carpets or washing dishes, activities which are heartily encouraged by his wife, who prefers shopping to housework. His hobbies include tennis, swimming, walking really fast and loon calling. Mendenhall sometimes dreams in numbers.

PENGUIN BOOKS

Published by the Penguin Group
Penguin Books Ltd, 27 Wrights Lane, London W8 5TZ, England
Penguin Books USA Inc., 375 Hudson Street, New York, New York 10014, USA
Penguin Books Australia Ltd, Ringwood, Victoria, Australia
Penguin Books Canada Ltd, 10 Alcorn Avenue, Toronto, Ontario, Canada M4V 3B2
Penguin Books (NZ) Ltd, 182–190 Wairau Road, Auckland 10, New Zealand

Penguin Books Ltd, Registered Offices: Harmondsworth, Middlesex, England

First published in the USA by Harper Perennial,
a division of Harper Collins Publishers, Inc., 1993
Published in Great Britain in Penguin Books 1993
1 3 5 7 9 10 8 6 4 2

Printed in England by Clays Ltd, St Ives plc

CAT PHYSICS

BY MENDENHALL

$$C = AT^2$$

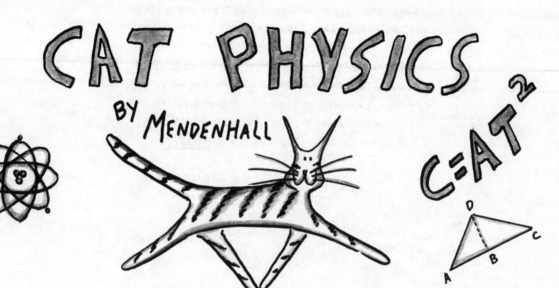

A CARTOON PRIMER

PENGUIN BOOKS

ALTHOUGH THIS BOOK IS TITLED <u>CAT PHYSICS</u>, THE
LAWS, PRINCIPLES, AXIOMS, POSTULATES AND THEOREMS
PRESENTED ARE DRAWN FROM MANY RELATED DISCI—
PLINES, INCLUDING CAT CHEMISTRY, CAT BIOLOGY,
CAT PSYCHOLOGY, CAT MEDICINE, CAT LOGIC, CAT
HISTORY, CAT MATHEMATICS AND CAT ENGINEERING.
THE AUTHOR DOES NOT INTEND TO DIMINISH THE
RICH CONTRIBUTIONS THESE RELATED DISCIPLINES
HAVE MADE TO THE STUDY OF <u>CAT PHYSICS</u>.

G.A. MENDENHALL

 ACKNOWLEDGMENTS

I WISH TO THANK MY WIFE MARY FOR HER TIRELESS LOVE
AND ENCOURAGEMENT, AND FOR TEACHING ME IT'S OK
TO BE IMPERFECT. SPECIAL THANKS TO JUDI SCHULER
WHOSE REMARKABLE ENERGY AND PERSISTENCE MADE THE
BOOK POSSIBLE. OF COURSE, MY THANKS TO TIGER, SUGAR
AND BLACKIE WHO TAUGHT ME ALL ABOUT CAT PHYSICS,
SERVED AS UNCOMPLAINING, UNDERPAID MODELS AND GAVE
ME THEIR UNLIMITED LOVE.

TIGER   SUGAR   BLACKIE

FAMOUS CATS IN PHYSICS HISTORY

ARCHIMEDES CAT   EINSTEIN CAT   NEWTON CAT

LAW OF CAT INERTIA

A CAT AT REST WILL TEND TO REMAIN AT REST — UNLESS ACTED UPON BY SOME OUTSIDE FORCE.

LAW OF CAT MOTION

A CAT WILL MOVE IN A STRAIGHT LINE — UNLESS THERE IS SOME REALLY GOOD REASON TO CHANGE DIRECTION.

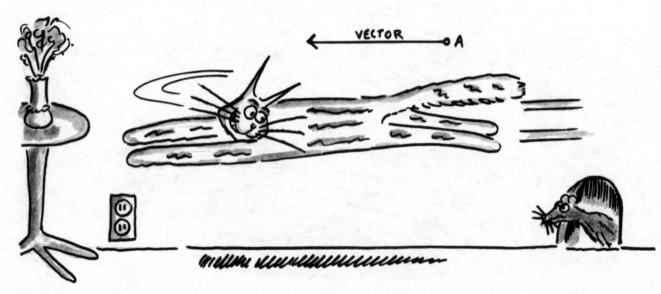

VECTOR   A

LAW OF CAT MAGNETISM

ALL BLUE BLAZERS AND BLACK SWEATERS ATTRACT CAT HAIR
IN DIRECT PROPORTION TO THE DARKNESS OF THE FABRIC.

LAW OF CAT THERMODYNAMICS

HEAT FLOWS FROM A WARMER TO A COOLER BODY— EXCEPT IN THE CASE OF A CAT— ALL HEAT FLOWS TO THE CAT.

LAW OF CAT STRETCHING

A CAT WILL STRETCH TO A DISTANCE PROPORTIONAL TO THE LENGTH OF THE NAP JUST TAKEN.

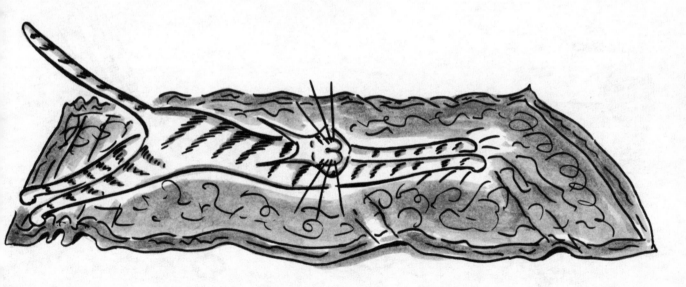

LAW OF CAT CONCENTRATION

A CAT'S CONCENTRATION WILL VARY IN DIRECT RELATION TO HIS INTEREST IN ANY GIVEN SUBJECT.

LAW OF CAT SLEEPING

ALL CATS MUST SLEEP WITH PEOPLE WHENEVER POSSIBLE.

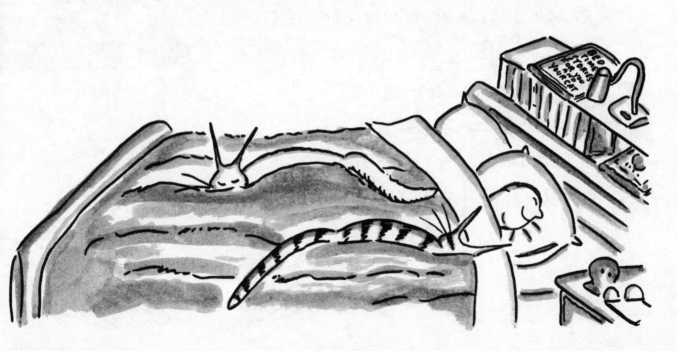

LAW OF CAT ACCELERATION

A CAT WILL ACCELERATE AT A CONSTANT SPEED — UNTIL HE GETS <u>GOOD</u> AND <u>READY</u> TO STOP.

LAW OF DINNER TABLE ATTENDANCE

CATS MUST ATTEND ALL MEALS WHERE ANYTHING GOOD IS SERVED.

LAW OF RUG CONFIGURATION

NO RUG MAY REMAIN IN ITS NATURALLY FLAT STATE — FOR VERY DARN LONG.

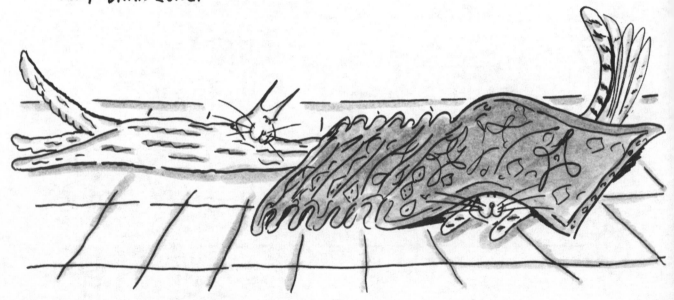

LAW OF OBEDIENCE RESISTANCE

A CAT'S RESISTANCE VARIES IN INVERSE PROPORTION TO HER DESIRE TO DO SOMETHING.

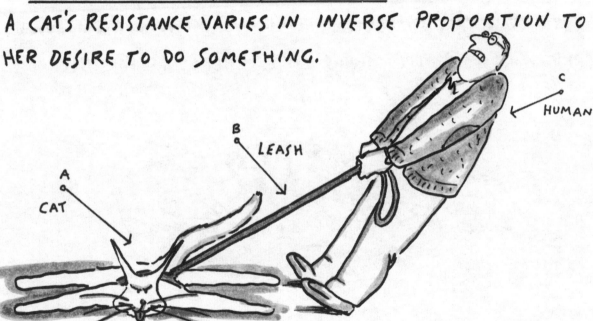

FIRST LAW OF ENERGY CONSERVATION

CATS KNOW THAT ENERGY CAN NEITHER BE CREATED NOR DESTROYED AND WILL THEREFORE USE AS LITTLE ENERGY AS POSSIBLE.

SECOND LAW OF ENERGY CONSERVATION

CATS ALSO KNOW THAT ENERGY CAN ONLY BE STORED — BY A LOT OF NAPPING.

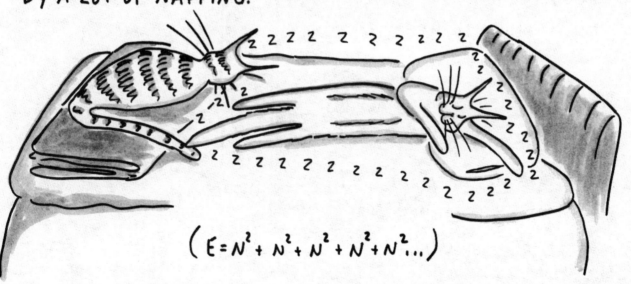

$$(E = N^2 + N^2 + N^2 + N^2 + N^2 \ldots)$$

LAW OF ELECTRIC BLANKET ATTRACTION

TURN ON AN ELECTRIC BLANKET, AND A CAT WILL
JUMP INTO BED AT THE SPEED OF LIGHT.

CLICK

LAW OF CAT PLAYING

THE MOST RAMBUNCTIOUS PLAYING TAKES PLACE
SOMETIME BETWEEN 3:15 A.M. AND 4:20 A.M.

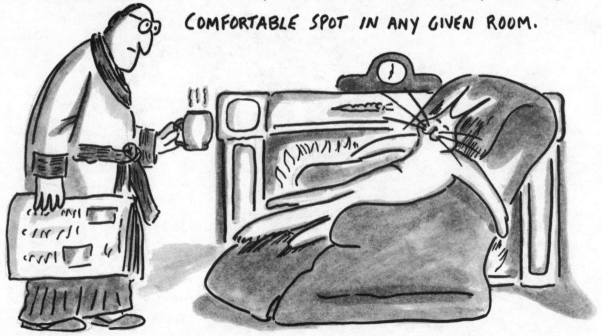

LAW OF RANDOM COMFORT SEEKING

A CAT WILL ALWAYS SEEK, AND USUALLY TAKE OVER, THE MOST COMFORTABLE SPOT IN ANY GIVEN ROOM.

FIRST LAW OF CAT BATHING

A CAT WILL TAKE A BATH ANYTIME AND ANYWHERE IT SEEMS CONVENIENT.

LAW OF ULTRALOW TEMPERATURES

A CAT REACHING ABSOLUTE ZERO WILL INSIST ON A HEATING PAD, A FIREPLACE AND A WARM LAP—IMMEDIATELY.

LAW OF SPACE OCCUPANCY

ALL BAGS IN A GIVEN ROOM MUST CONTAIN A CAT WITHIN THE EARLIEST POSSIBLE NANOSECOND.

LAW OF UNIT MEASUREMENT

ONE CAT FOOT POUND IS THE AMOUNT OF WORK NEEDED TO LIFT ONE POUND ONE FOOT — BUT CATS NEVER WORK.

LAW OF CAT EMBARRASSMENT

A CAT'S IRRITATION RISES IN DIRECT PROPORTION TO HER EMBARRASSMENT TIMES THE AMOUNT OF HUMAN LAUGHTER.

LAW OF MILK CONSUMPTION

A CAT WILL DRINK HIS WEIGHT IN MILK SQUARED—JUST TO SHOW YOU HE CAN.

LAW OF FURNITURE REPLACEMENT

CATS' DESIRE TO SCRATCH FURNITURE IS DIRECTLY PROPORTIONAL TO THE COST OF THE FURNITURE.

LAW OF CIRCULAR MOTION

A CAT WILL FOLLOW AN OBJECT MOVING IN A FIXED CIRCULAR PATH — AND HER TAIL WILL DO THE SAME.

A
CAT

B
OBJECT

C
OTHER
TOYS

FIRST LAW OF CAT LANDING

A CAT CAN LAND IN AN AREA (C) EQUAL TO ⅓ THE ARCH OF HIS BACK (AX) OR ⅓ THE LENGTH OF HIS TAIL (BY) TIMES PI (π).

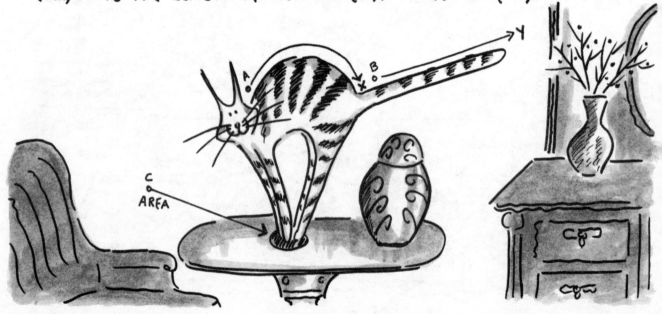

SECOND LAW OF CAT LANDING

A CAT WILL ALWAYS LAND IN THE SOFTEST PLACE POSSIBLE.

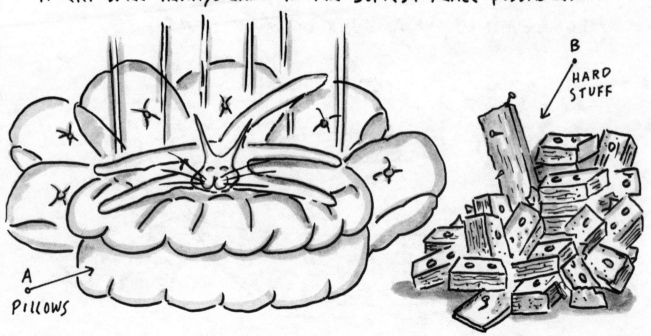

A
PILLOWS

B
HARD
STUFF

LAW OF FLUID DISPLACEMENT

A CAT IMMERSED IN MILK WILL DISPLACE HER OWN
VOLUME — MINUS THE AMOUNT OF MILK CONSUMED.

C
CAT

B
SMALL MILK
BOWL

A
BIG MILK
BOWL

MILK

MILK

LAW OF CAT DISINTEREST

A CAT'S INTEREST LEVEL OFTEN VARIES IN INVERSE PROPORTION TO THE AMOUNT OF EFFORT YOU EXPEND.

FIRST LAW OF TAIL ANGLES

THE ANGLE OF A CAT'S TAIL WILL EQUAL OR EXCEED 90° WHEN HE'S CONTENT, AND WILL BE LESS THAN 90° WHEN HE'S NOT.

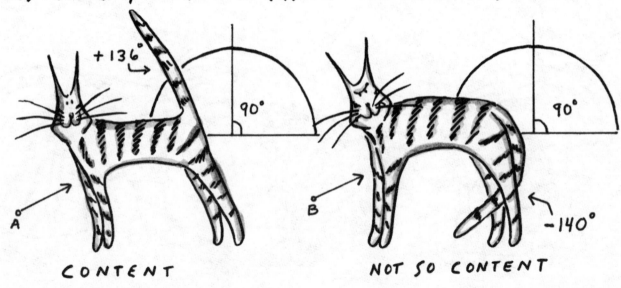

CONTENT   NOT SO CONTENT

SECOND LAW OF TAIL ANGLES

WHEN A CAT'S TAIL IS THE HYPOTENUSE OF A RIGHT TRIANGLE, ITS LENGTH IS THE SUM OF THE SQUARES OF THE OTHER TWO SIDES OR $AB^2 + BC^2 = AC^2$.

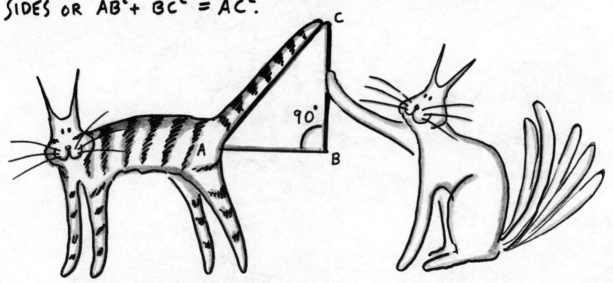

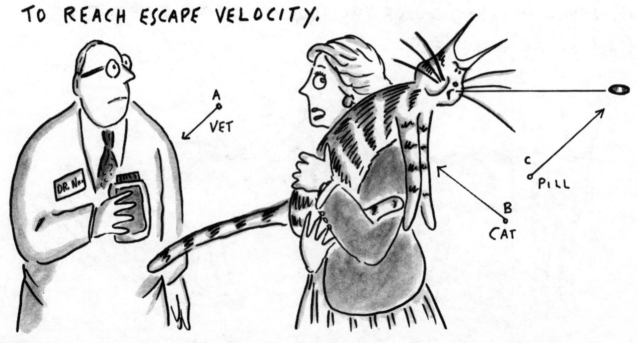

LAW OF DISCRETE PARTICLES

A CAT WILL TOLERATE DISCRETE PARTICLES ONLY IF THEY ARE PROPERLY CONTAINED IN A CLEAN LITTER BOX.

LAW OF SHOT AVOIDANCE

A CAT WILL DO JUST ABOUT ANYTHING TO AVOID A SHOT.

LAW OF CAT COMPOSITION

CATS ARE COMPOSED OF THE FOLLOWING:

MATTER   ANTI-MATTER AND   IT DOESN'T MATTER

LAW OF EQUIDISTANT SEPARATION

ALL CATS IN A GIVEN ROOM WILL LOCATE AT POINTS EQUIDISTANT FROM EACH OTHER, AND EQUIDISTANT FROM THE CENTER OF THE ROOM.

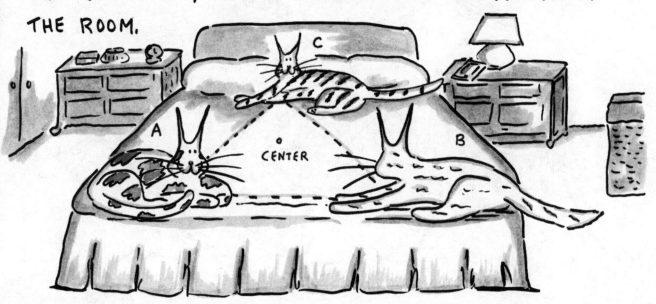

LAW OF CAT NIGHT VISION
A CAT CAN SEE IN THE DARK — AND YOU CAN'T.

LAW OF CHAIN REACTION

WHEN A SMALL, FURRY ANIMAL (C) TRAVELS IN A CONTINUOUS
PATH BETWEEN CAT A AND CAT B, THE REACTION IS SELF-SUSTAINING.

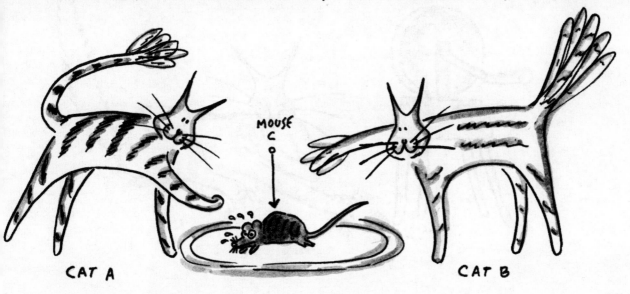

MOUSE
C

CAT A

CAT B

LAW OF CLAW SHARPENING

ALL CLAWS MUST BE SHARPENED TO THE LAST POSSIBLE
NUCLEUS OF THE LAST POSSIBLE ATOM.

LAW OF CAT CAUTION

A CAT WILL ALWAYS FIND THE SAFEST SPOT IN ANY GIVEN ROOM — NO MATTER WHAT PEOPLE THINK.

LAW OF CAT DIGNITY

ALL CATS MAINTAIN THE MAXIMUM AMOUNT OF GRACE
AND DIGNITY—NO MATTER WHAT THE SITUATION.

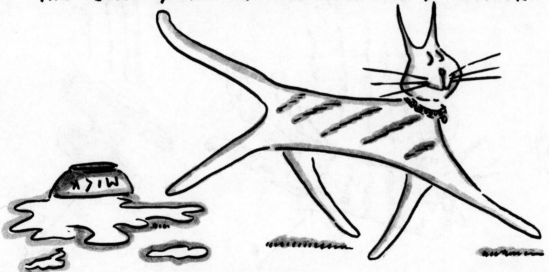

FIRST LAW OF CAT GRAVITY

A CAT WILL FALL AT THE SAME RATE AS ANY OTHER OBJECT— EXCEPT CATS HARDLY EVER FALL.

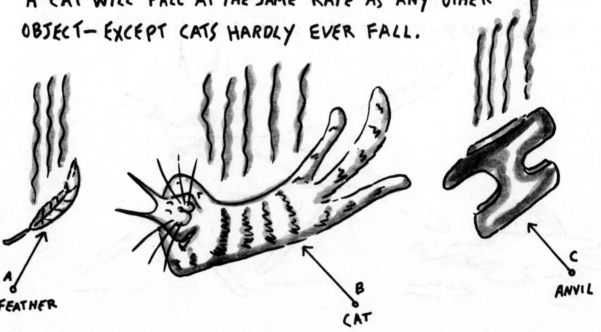

A FEATHER

B CAT

C ANVIL

SECOND LAW OF CAT GRAVITY

ALL CATS ARE EXEMPT FROM THE ORDINARY LAWS OF GRAVITY.

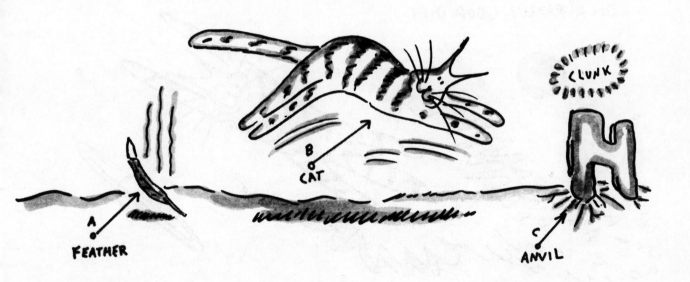

SPECIAL LAW OF MASS AND VELOCITY

A CAT TRAVELING AT OR NEAR THE SPEED OF LIGHT WILL
BECOME GEOMETRICALLY MORE MASSIVE — UNLESS HE IS
ON A REALLY GOOD DIET.

SPACE-TIME CONTINUUM

GIVEN ENOUGH TIME, A CAT WILL LAND IN JUST ABOUT ANY SPACE.

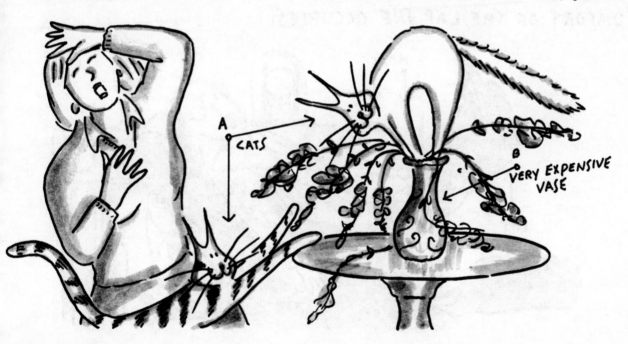

A
CATS

B
VERY EXPENSIVE
VASE

LAW OF CONCENTRATION OF MASS

A CAT'S MASS INCREASES IN DIRECT PROPORTION TO THE COMFORT OF THE LAP *SHE* OCCUPIES.

LAW OF CAT PROPORTION

THE ARCH OF A CAT'S BACK IS EQUAL TO THE DISTANCE BETWEEN HIS FEET DIVIDED BY PI UNLESS...

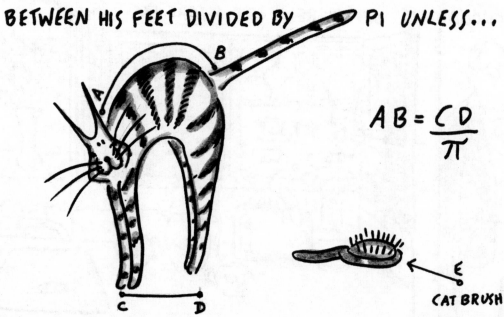

$$AB = \frac{CD}{\pi}$$

CAT BRUSH

THAT CAT IS ENJOYING A FABULOUS BRUSHING.

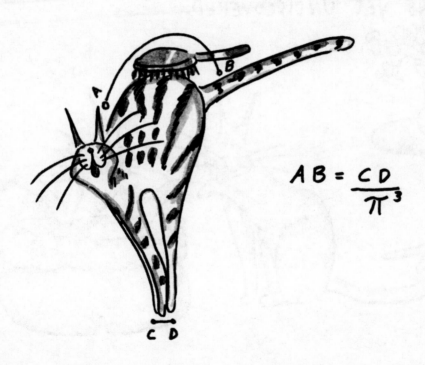

$$AB = \frac{CD}{\pi^3}$$

LAW OF CAT OBEDIENCE

AS YET UNDISCOVERED.

WAVE THEORY
IT'S IMPOSSIBLE TO TEACH A CAT TO WAVE BYE-BYE.

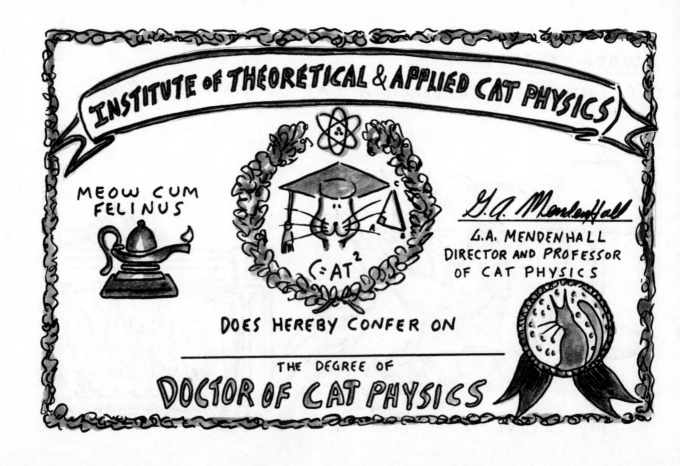